LEVEL TWO

christmas music

By David Carr Glover

Part I of this book, Christmas Music, contains traditional Christmas music along with passages from the bible pertaining to the story of Christmas.

Part II is a continuation of traditional Christmas music.

PART I
The Christmas Story

PART II

The Christmas Story

O Come, All Ye Faithful

Processional

OLD LATIN HYMN
Tr. by FREDERICK OAKELEY

JOHN READING

Stanza 2
Sing, choirs of angels, sing in exultation,
O sing, all ye bright hosts of heav'n above;
Glory to God, all glory in the highest.

Refrain

Stanza 3
Yea, Lord, we greet Thee, born this happy morning,
Jesus, to Thee be all glory giv'n;
Word of the Father, now in flesh appearing.

Refrain

MATTHEW 1: 20 - 23

Behold, the angel of the Lord appeared unto Joseph in a dream, saying, Joseph, thou son of David, fear not to take unto thee Mary thy wife; for that which is conceived in her is of the Holy Ghost. And she shall bring forth a son, and thou shalt call his name Jesus; for he shall save his people from their sins. Now all this was done, that it might be fulfilled which was spoken of the Lord by the prophet, saying; Behold, a virgin shall be with child, and shall bring forth a son, and they shall call his name Emmanuel; which being interpreted is, God with us.

O Come, O Come Emmanuel

Latin Antiphons, XI Century
Latin Hymn, XVII Century
Tr. by JOHN MASON NEALE, 1851, 1861

ANCIENT PLAIN SONG

Stanza 3
O come, Thou Day-spring, come and cheer
Our spirits by Thine advent here;
And drive away the shades of night,
And pierce the clouds and bring us light!
Rejoice! rejoice! Emmanuel
Shall come to thee, O Israel!

Stanza 4
O come, Thou Key of David, come,
And open wide our heavenly home;
Make safe the way that leads on high,
And close the path to misery.
Rejoice! rejoice! Emmanuel
Shall come to thee, O Israel!

LUKE 2: 1 - 7

And it came to pass in those days, that there went out a decree from Cesar Augustus, that all the world should be taxed. And this taxing was first made when Cyrenius was governor of Syria. And all went to be taxed, every one into his own city. And Joseph also went up from Galilee, out of the city of Nazareth, into Judea, unto the city of David, which is called Bethlehem, because he was of the house and lineage of David, To be taxed with Mary his espoused wife, being great with child. And so it was, that, while they were there, the days were accomplished that she should be delivered. And she brought forth her first-born son, and wrapped him in swaddling-clothes, and laid him in a manger; because there was no room for them in the inn.

Silent Night

JOSEPH MOHR

FRANZ GRUBER

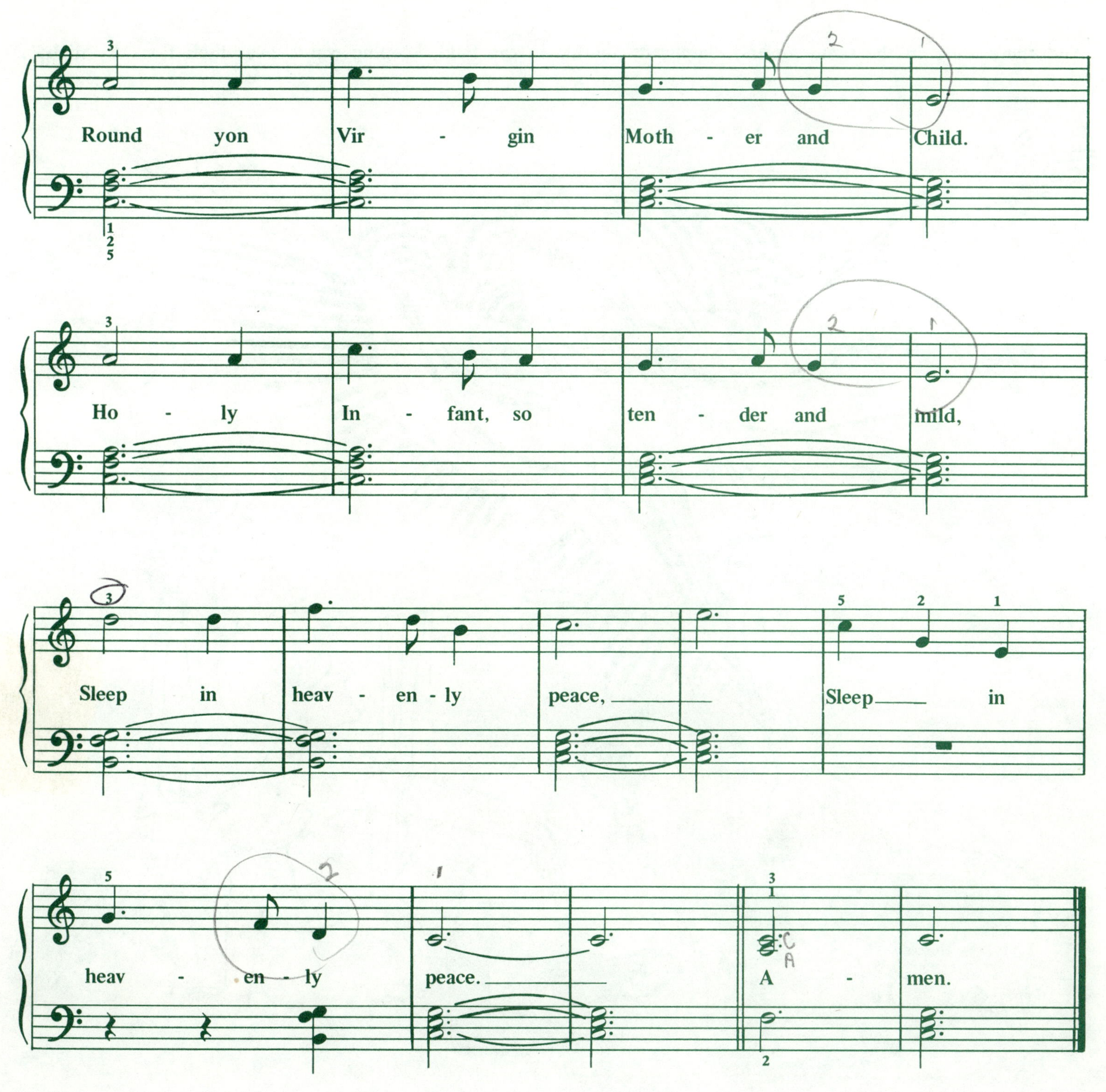

Stanza 2
Silent night! Holy night!
Shepherds quake at the sight!
Glories stream from heaven a-far,
Heavenly hosts sing Alleluia;
Christ the Saviour is born,
Christ the Saviour is born.

Stanza 3
Silent night! Holy night!
Son of God, love's pure light
Radiant beams from Thy holy face,
With the dawn of redeeming grace,
Jesus, Lord, at Thy birth,
Jesus, Lord, at Thy birth.

LUKE 2: 8
And there were in the same country shepherds abiding in the field, keeping watch over their flock by night.

While Shepherds Watched Their Flocks

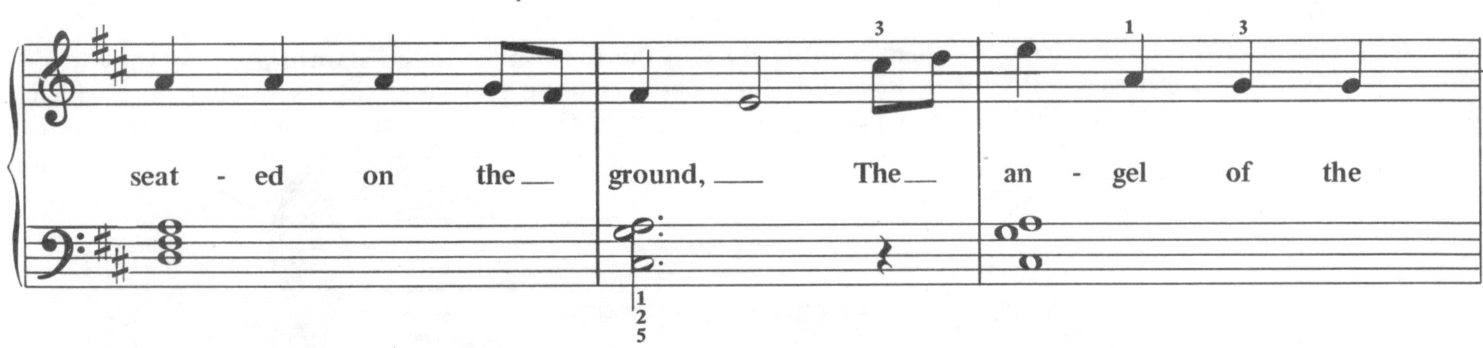

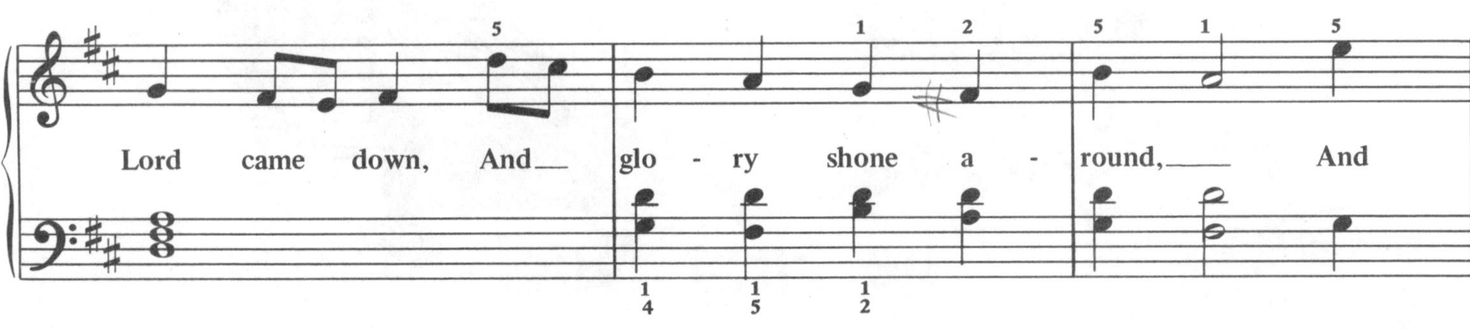

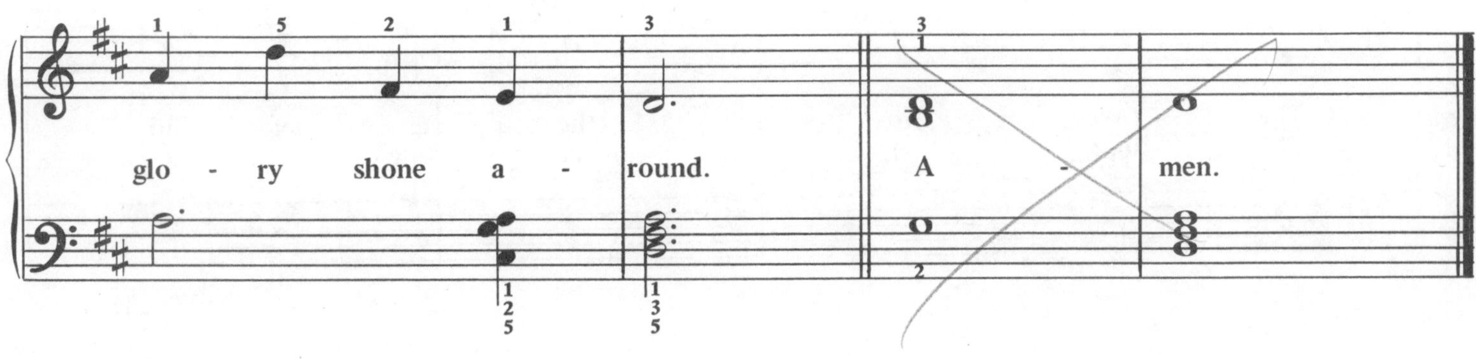

Stanza 2
"Fear not", said he; for mighty dread
Had seized their troubled mind,
"Glad tidings of great joy I bring,
To you and all mankind,
To you and all mankind."

Stanza 3
"To you, in David's town, this day
Is born, of David's line,
The Saviour, who is Christ the Lord;
And this shall be the sign,
And this shall be the sign."

Stanza 4
"The heav'nly Babe you there shall find
To human view displayed,
All meanly wrapped in swathing bands,
And in a manger laid,
And in a manger laid."

Stanza 5
"All glory be to God on high,
And to the earth be peace;
Good-will henceforth from heav'n to 'men
Begin, and never cease,
Begin, and never cease!"

LUKE 2: 9 - 11

And, lo, the angel of the Lord came upon them, and the glory of the Lord shone round about them; and they were sore afraid. And the angel said unto them, Fear not: for, behold, I bring you good tidings of great joy, which shall be to all people. For unto you is born this day, in the city of David, a Saviour, which is Christ the Lord.

Stanza 3
This star drew nigh to the north-west,
O'er Bethlehem it took its rest,
And there it did both stop and stay
Right Over the place where Jesus lay.

Chorus:

Stanza 4
Then enter'd in there Wise Men three,
Full rev'rently upon their knee,
And offer'd there in His presence
Their gold and myrrh and frank-in-cense.

Chorus:

LUKE 2: 12 - 14

And this shall be a sign unto you; Ye shall find the babe wrapped in swaddling clothes, lying in a manger. And suddenly there was with the angel a multitude of heavenly host praising God, and saying, Glory to God in the highest, and on earth peace, good-will toward men.

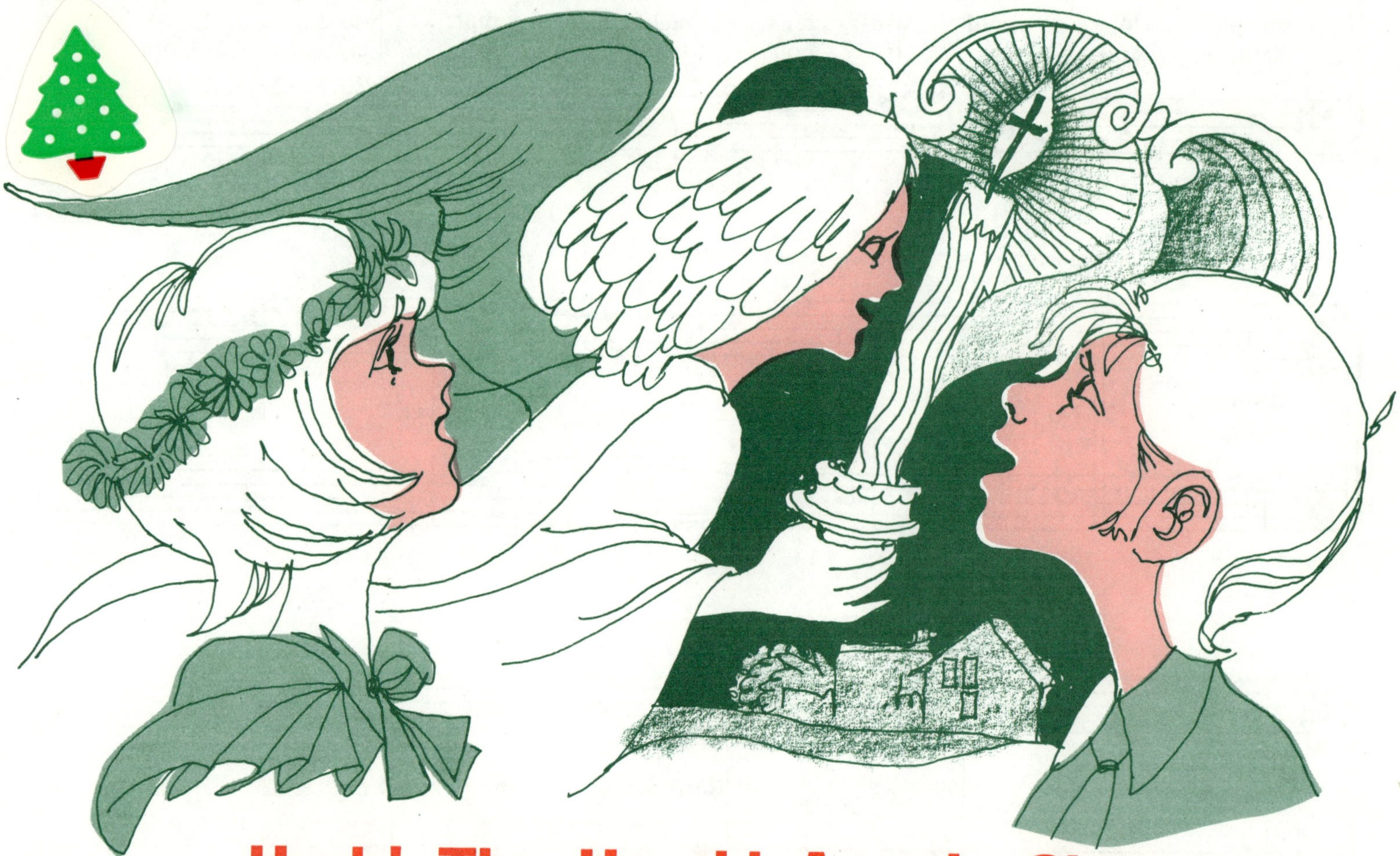

Hark! The Herald Angels Sing

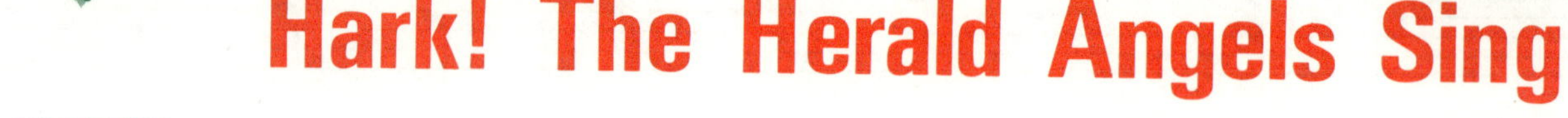

C. WESLEY
Alt. by M. MADAN

FELIX MENDELSSOHN

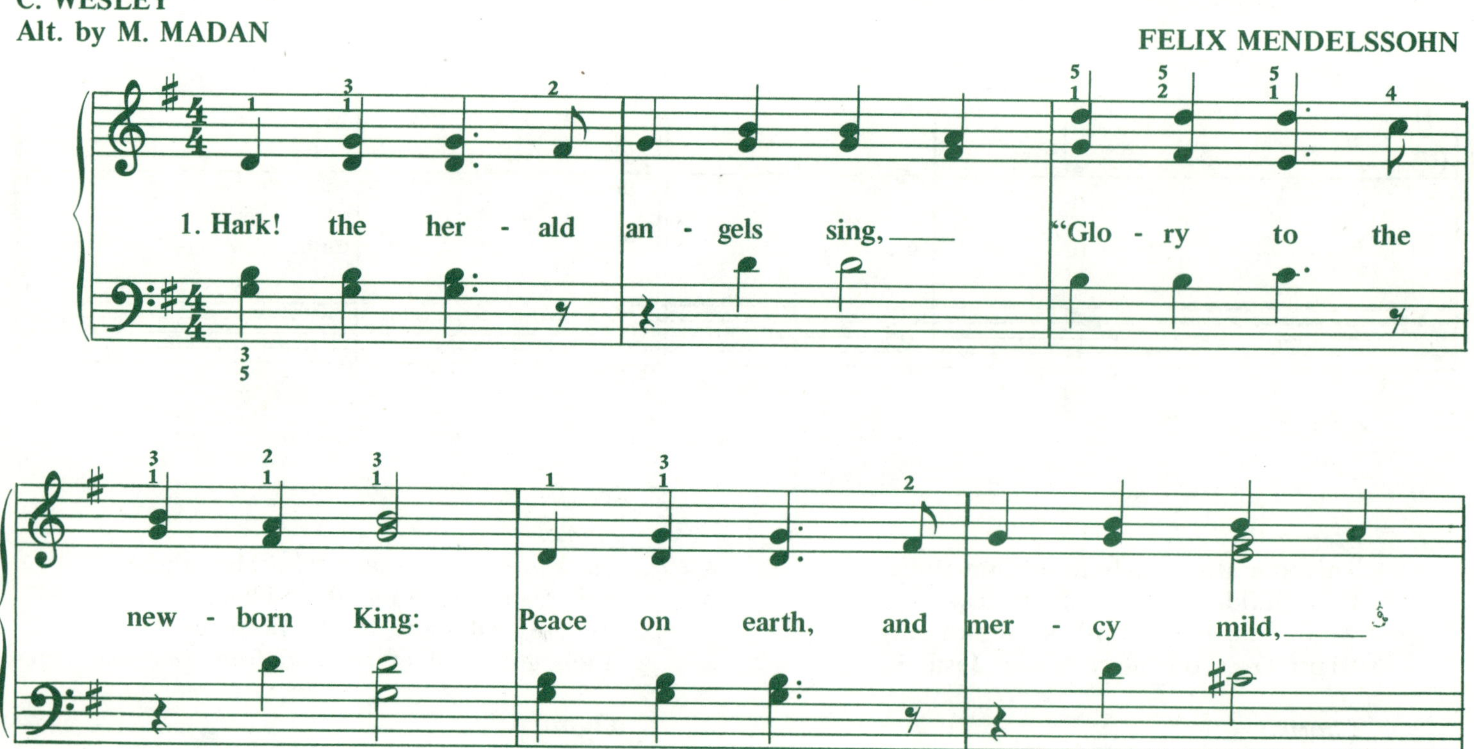

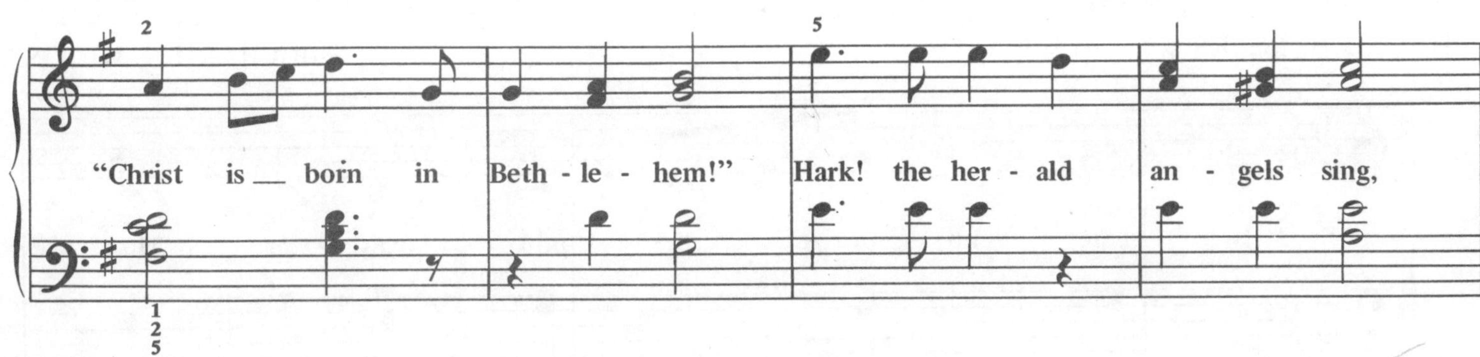

Stanza 2
Christ, by highest heaven adored;
Christ, the Everlasting Lord!
Late in time behold Him come,
Off-spring of the Virgin's womb:
Veiled in flesh the God-head see;
Hail th' Incarnate Deity,
Pleased as man with men to dwell,
Jesus, our Emmanuel.
Hark! the herald angels sing,
"Glory to the new-born King."

Stanza 3
Hail the heaven-born Prince of Peace!
Hail the Sun of Righteousness!
Light and life to all He brings,
Risen with healing in His wings.
Mild He lays His glory by,
Born that man no more may die,
Born to raise the sons of earth,
Born to give them second birth.
Hark! the hearald angels sing.
"Glory to the new-born King."

LUKE 2: 15

And it came to pass, as the angels were gone away from them into heaven, the shepherds said one to another, Let us now go even unto Bethlehem, and see this thing which is come to pass, which the Lord hath made known unto us.

It Came Upon The Midnight Clear

EDMUND H. SEARS

RICHARD S. WILLIS

1. It came up - on ___ the mid - night clear, That

glo - rious song ___ of old, ___ From an - gels bend - ing

near the earth To touch their harps ___ of gold: ___ "Peace

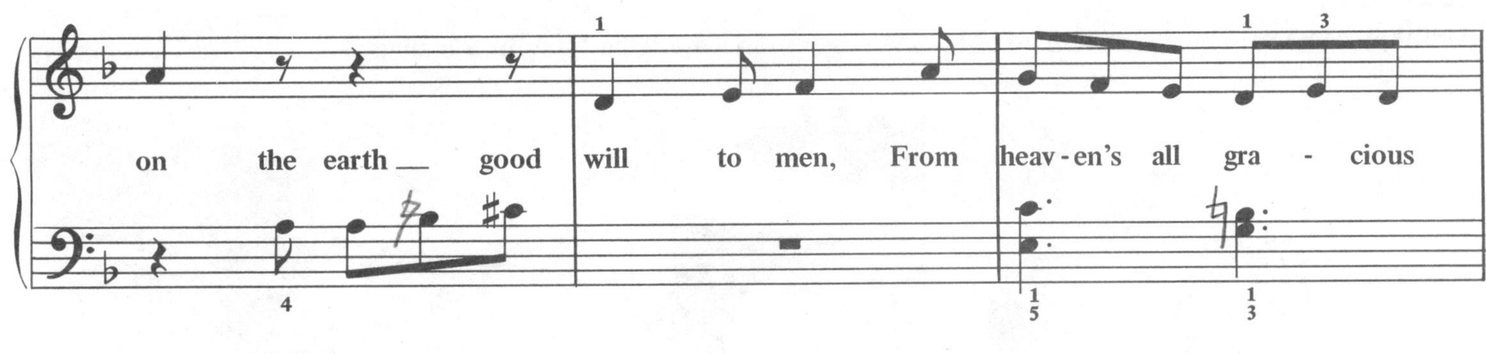

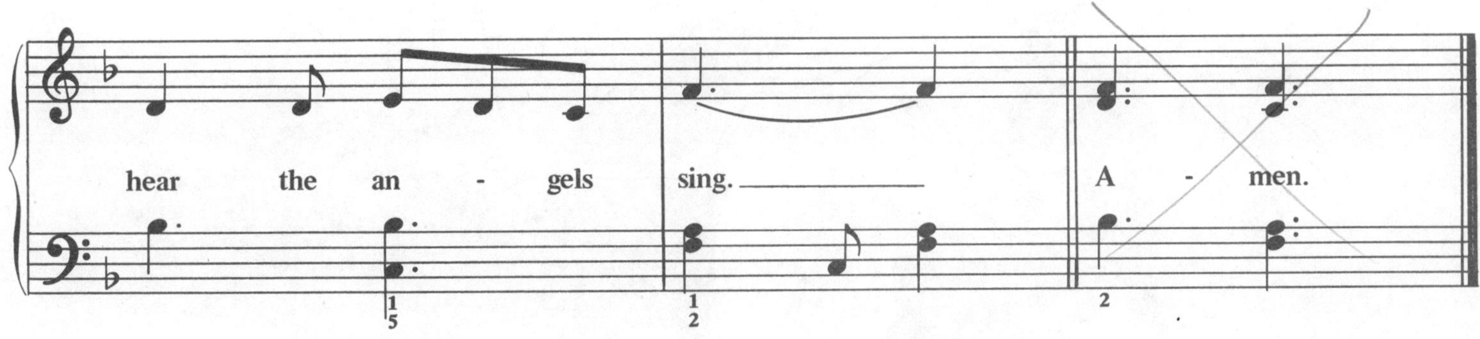

Stanza 2
Still through the cloven skies they come,
With peaceful wings unfurled,
And still their heavenly music floats
O'er all the weary world:
Above its sad and lowly plains
They bend on hovering wing:
And ever o'er its Babel sounds
The blessed angels sing.

Stanza 3
And ye, beneath life's crushing load.
Whose forms are bending low,
Who toil along the climbing way
With painful steps and slow,
Look now! for glad and golden hours
Come swiftly on the wing;
O rest beside the weary road,
And hear the angels sing.

Stanza 4
For lo, the days are hastening on,
By prophet-bards foretold,
When, with the ever-circling years,
Comes round the age of gold:
When peace shall over all the earth
Its ancient splendors fling,
And the whole world give back the song
Which now the angels sing.

LUKE 2: 16
And they came with haste, and found Mary and Joseph, and the babe lying in a manger.

Away In A Manger

MARTIN LUTHER

CARL MUELLER

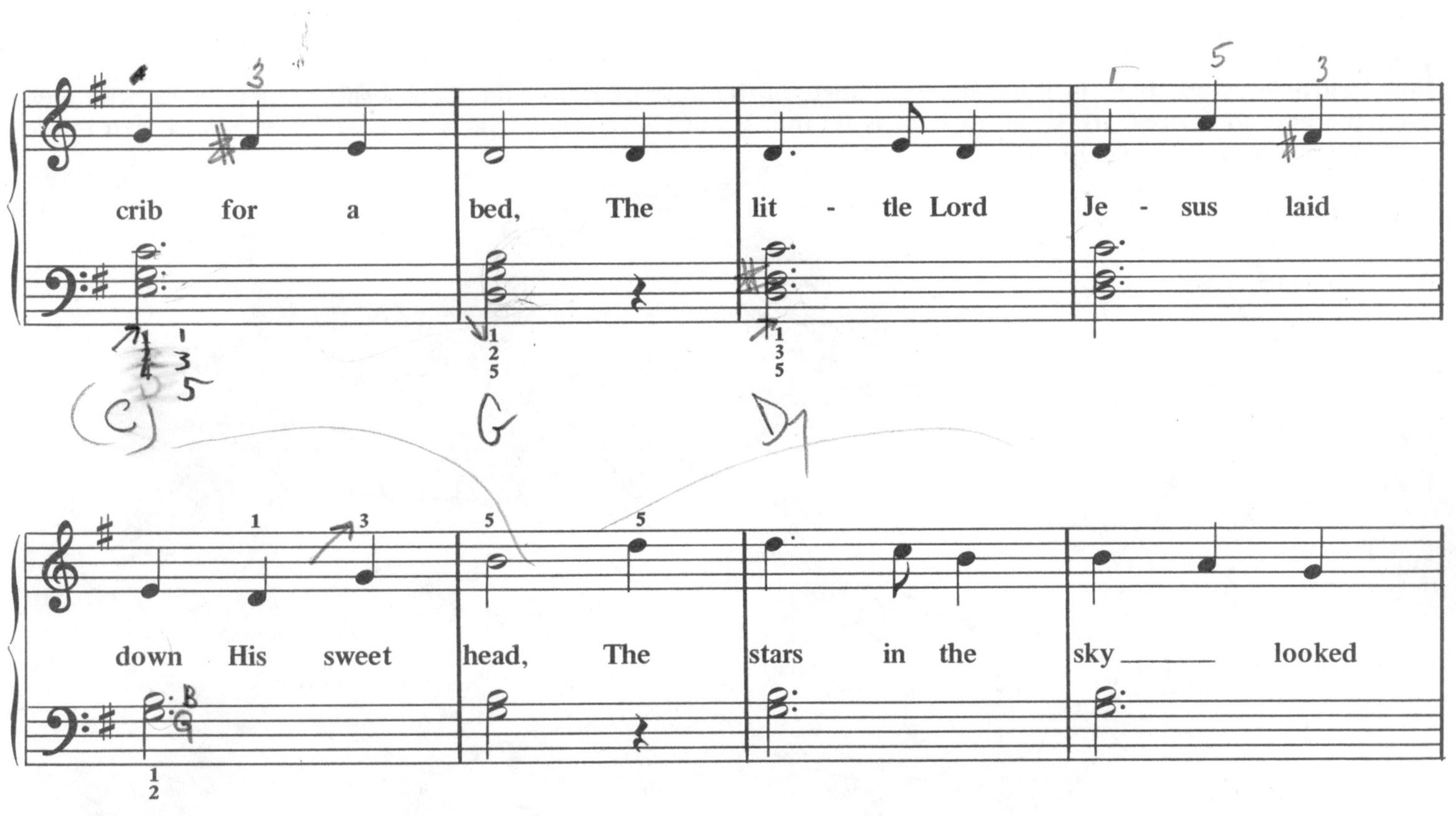

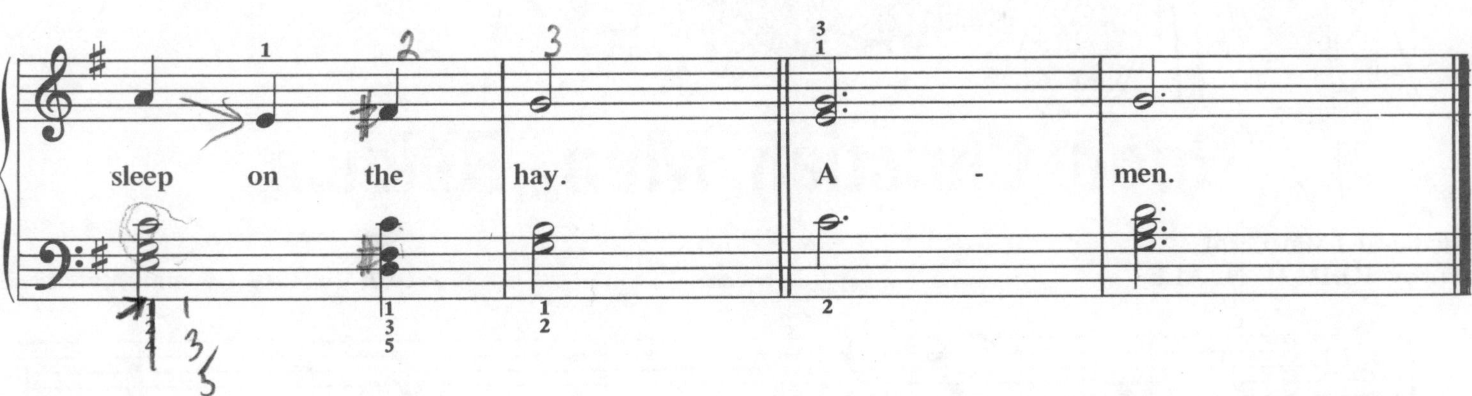

Stanza 2
The cattle are lowing, the Baby awakes,
But little Lord Jesus no crying He makes.
I love Thee, Lord Jesus, look down from the sky,
And stay by my side until morning is nigh.

Stanza 3
Be near me, Lord Jesus; I ask Thee to stay,
Close by me forever, and love me, I pray.
Bless all the dear children in Thy tender care,
And fit us for heaven to live with Thee there.

MATTHEW 2: 1 - 2

Now, when Jesus was born in Bethlehem of Judea, in the days of Herod the King, behold, there came wise men from the east to Jerusalem, Saying, Where is he that is born King of the Jews? for we have seen his star in the east, and are come to worship him.

Good Christian Men, Rejoice

Medieval Latin Carol
Tr. by JOHN M. NEALE

14th Century German Melody

Stanza 2
Good Christian men, rejoice
With heart, and soul, and voice;
Now ye hear of endless bliss;
Joy! joy! Jesus Christ was born for this!
He has opened the heavenly door,
And man is blessed ever-more
Christ was born for this!
Christ was born for this!

Stanza 3
Good Christian men, rejoice
With heart, and soul, and voice;
Now ye need not fear the grave;
Peace! peace! Jesus Christ was born to save!
Calls you one and calls you all,
To gain His ever-lasting hall.
Christ was born to save!
Christ was born to save!

MATTHEW 2: 3 - 6

When Herod the King had heard these things, he was troubled, and all Jerusalem with him. And when he had gathered all the chief priests and scribes of the people together, he demanded of them where Christ should be born. And they said unto him, In Bethlehem of Judea: for thus it is written by the prophet. And thou Bethlehem, In the land of Judah, art not the least among the princes of Juda: for out of thee shall come a Governor, that shall rule my people Israel.

O Little Town Of Bethlehem

PHILLIPS BROOKS

LEWIS H. REDNER

Stanza 2
For Christ is born of Mary;
And gathered all above,
While mortals sleep, the angels keep
Their watch of wond'ring love.
O morning stars, together
Proclaim the holy birth;
And praises sing to God the King,
And peace to men on earth.

Stanza 3
How silently, how silently,
The wondrous gift is giv'n!
So God imparts to human hearts
The blessings of His heav'n.
No ear may hear His coming,
But in this world of sin,
Where meek souls will receive Him still,
The dear Christ enters in.

Stanza 4
O holy Child of Bethlehem,
Descend on us, we pray;
Cast out our sin, and enter in,
Be born in us today.
We hear the Christmas angels
The great glad tidings tell;
O come to us, abide with us,
Our Lord Emmanuel.

MATTHEW 2: 7 - 10

Then Herod, when he had privily called the wise men, inquired of them diligently what time the star appeared. And he sent them to Bethlehem, and said, Go and search diligently for the young child; and when ye have found him, bring me word again, that I may come and worship him also. When they had heard the king, they departed; and lo, the star; which they saw in the east, went before them, till it came and stood where the young child was. When they saw the star, they rejoiced with exceeding great joy.

As With Gladness Men Of Old

WILLIAM C. DIX

CONRAD KOCHER

Stanza 2
As with joyful steps they sped
To that lowly manger bed,
There to bend the knee before
Him whom heaven and earth adore;
So may we with willing feet
Ever seek thy mercy seat.

Stanza 3
As they offered gifts most rare,
At that manger rude and bare,
So may we with holy joy,
Pure and free from sin's alloy,
All our costliest treasures bring,
Christ, to thee, our heavenly King.

Stanza 4
Holy Jesus, every day
Keep us in the narrow way;
And, when earthly things are past,
Bring our ransomed souls at last
Where they need no star to guide,
Where no clouds thy glory hide.

MATTHEW 2: 11

And when they were come into the house, they saw the young child with Mary his mother; and fell down and worshipped him: and when they had opened their treasures, they presented unto him gifts; gold, and frankincense, and myrrh.

We Three Kings

REV. JOHN H. HOPKINS

J.H.H.

1. We three kings of O - ri - ent are;
Bear - ing gifts we trav - erse a - far
Field and foun - tain, moor and moun - tain,
Fol - low - ing yon - der star.

Refrain

O

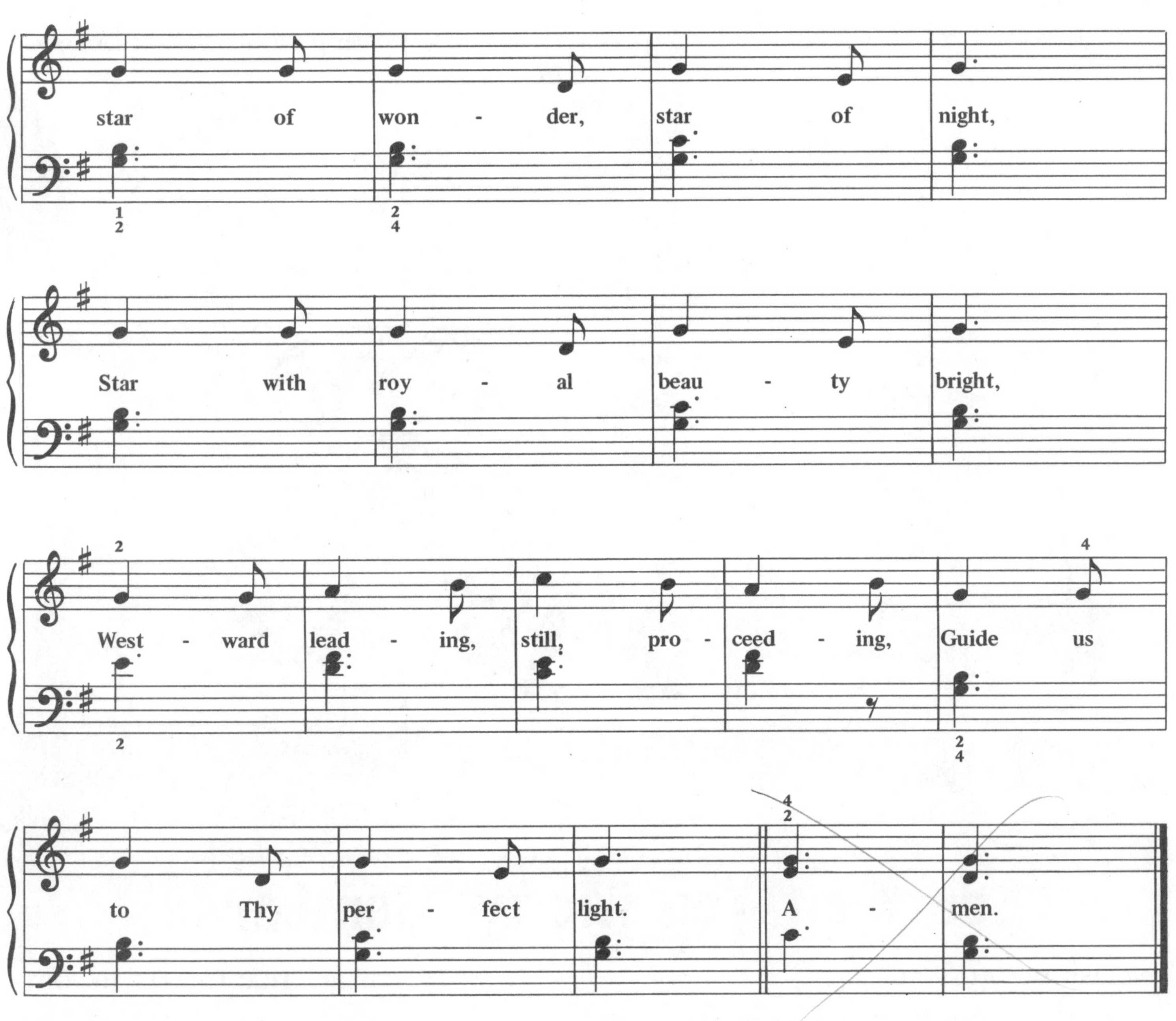

Stanza 2
Born a King on Bethlehem's plain,
Gold I bring to crown Him again,
King for-ever, ceasing never
Over us all to reign.

Refrain

Stanza 3
Frank-incense to offer have I;
Incense owns a Deity nigh;
Prayer and praising all men raising,
Worship Him, God on high.

Refrain

Stanza 4
Myrrh is mine: its bitter perfume
Breathes a life of gathering gloom:
Sorrowing, sighing, bleeding, dying,
Sealed in the stone-cold tomb.

Refrain

Stanza 5
Glorious now behold Him arise,
King and God and Sacrifice;
Alleluia, Alleluia!
Sounds through the earth and skies.

Refrain

MATTHEW 2: 12

And being warned of God in a dream that they should not return to Herod, they departed into their own country another way.

God Rest You Merry, Gentlemen

ENGLISH TRADITIONAL

TRADITIONAL MELODY

Stanza 2
From God our heavenly Father
A blessed angel came;
And unto certain shepherds
Brought tidings of the same;
How that in Bethlehem was born
The Son of God by name.

Refrain

Stanza 3
"Fear now, then," said the angel,
"Let nothing you affright,
This day is born a Saviour
Of a pure Virgin bright,
To free all those who trust in Him
From Satan's power and might."

Refrain

Stanza 4
Now to the Lord sing praises,
All you within this place,
And with true love and brother-hood
Each other now embrace;
This holy tide of Christmas
All others doth deface.

Refrain

Joy To The World

Recessional

ISSAC WATTS

GEORGE F. HANDEL

Stanza 2
Joy to the earth! the Saviour reigns;
Let men their songs employ;
While fields and floods, rocks, hills, and plains
Repeat the sounding joy,
Repeat the sounding joy,
Repeat, repeat the sounding joy.

Stanza 3
No more let sins and sorrows grow,
Nor thorns infest the ground;
He comes to make His blessings flow
Far as the curse is found,
Far as the curse is found,
Far as, far as the curse is found.

Stanza 4
He rules the world with truth and grace,
And makes the nations prove
The glories of His righteousness,
And wonders of His love,
And wonders of His love,
And wonders, wonders of His love,

Angels, From The Realms Of Glory

JAMES MONTGOMERY HENRY SMART

Stanza 2
Shepherds, in the field abiding,
Watching o'er your flocks by night,
God with man is now residing;
Yonder shines the infant light:
Come and worship, come and worship,
Worship Christ, the newborn King.

Stanza 3
Sages, leave your contemplations,
Brighter visions beam a-far;
Seek the great Desire of nations;
Ye have seen His natal star:
Come and worship, come and worship,
Worship Christ, the newborn King.

Stanza 4
Saints, before the altar bending,
Watching long in hope and fear,
Suddenly the Lord, descending,
In His temple shall appear:
Come and worship, come and worship,
Worship Christ, the newborn King.

Stanza 5
Sinners, wrung with true repentance,
Doomed for guilt to endless pains,
Justice now revokes the sentence,
Mercy calls you, break your chains:
Come and worship, come and worship,
Worship Christ, the newborn King.

Once In Royal David's City

CECIL F. ALEXANDER

HENRY J. GAUNTLETT

Stanza 2
He came down to earth from heaven
Who is God and Lord of all,
And His shelter was a stable,
And His cradle was a stall:
With the poor, and mean, and lowly,
Lived on earth our Saviour holy.

Stanza 3
Jesus is our childhood's pattern.
Day by day like us He grew;
He was little, weak, and helpless,
Tears and smiles like us He knew:
And He feeleth for our sadness,
And He shareth in our gladness.

Stanza 4
And our eyes at last shall see Him,
Through His own redeeming love;
For that Child so dear and gentle
Is our Lord in heaven above,
And He leads His children on
To the place where He is gone. Amen.

I Heard The Bells On Christmas Day

HENRY W. LONGFELLOW

J. BAPTISTE CALKIN

Stanza 2
I thought how, as the day had come.
The belfries of all Christendom
Had rolled along the unbroken song
Of peace on earth, good-will to men.

Stanza 3
And in despair I bowed my head:
'There is no peace on earth,' I said,
'For hate is strong, and mocks the song
Of peace on earth, good-will to men.'

Stanza 4
Then pealed the bells more loud and deep:
'God is not dead, nor doth he sleep;
The wrong shall fail, the right prevail,
With peace on earth, good-will to men':

Stanza 5
Till, ringing, singing on its way,
The world revolved from night to day,
A voice, a chime, a chant sublime,
Of peace on earth, good-will to men!